Sid

I am Sid.

Sid taps the tin.

Sid is in the tin.

Sid sips.

Sid sits.

Nat pats Sid.

Sid naps.

Before reading

Say the sounds: s a t p i n m d

Practise blending the sounds: Sid taps tin sips sits pats Nat naps

High-frequency words: in am **Tricky words:** the I is

Vocabulary check: nap – What happens when someone has a nap?
tin – What is a tin? (short for tin can) What are some things you can buy in a
tin? What is tin? (a shiny metal)

Story discussion: Look at the cover. Who is this story about? What can you tell
about this cat? What are some of the things that cats do?

Teaching points: Talk about the verb "pat" and how the addition of "s" at
the end of a verb changes who does the action, e.g. they pat/he pats and
they nap/she naps.

After reading

Comprehension:
- What does Sid like to do with the tin?
- What did Sid do at his water bowl?
- What did Nat do with the cat?
- Do you think Sid liked getting a pat? What makes you say that?

Fluency: Speed read the words again from the inside front cover.